Mal and Chad

Stephen McCranie

The BIGGEST, BESTEST TIME EVER!

SCHOLASTIC INC.

For my dad.

ISBN 978-0-545-58804-1

12 11 10 9 8 7 6 5 4 3 2 1   13 14 15 16 17 18/0

Printed in the U.S.A.   23

First Scholastic printing, March 2013

Edited by Michael Green
Designed by Richard Amari

CHAPTER 1
Captain Porky! Come Back!

ALL THE KIDS ON MY BUS ARE MEAN TO ME, SO INSTEAD OF RIDING THE BUS TO SCHOOL, I'M GOING TO START FLYING TO SCHOOL!

THEN, WHEN I GET THERE, I CAN EASILY DISGUISE THIS JET PACK AS A BACKPACK, AND NO ONE WILL BE THE WISER!

COOL, HUH?

UM, MAL, ISN'T TAKING THE BUS A LITTLE MORE...

...SAFE?

I'LL BE FINE.

THERE... ALL FINISHED!

YOU SHOULD TEST IT OUT FIRST...

I MEAN, BEFORE YOU ACTUALLY FLY IT YOURSELF.

WHAT, DO YOU WANT TO TEST IT OUT FOR ME?

BUT THAT BACKPACK HAD MY HOMEWORK IN IT...

...AND MY TEXTBOOKS...

≡sniff≡

...AND MY LUNCH.

NO... NOT-- THE LUNCH!

CAPTAIN PORKY! COME BACK!

9

YOU LOST YOUR LUNCH?

HOW?

UM...

I...

SCREECH!

!

OH GOSH!

MY BUS IS HERE!

≶sigh≶

MAL, YOU NEED TO KEEP TRACK OF YOUR STUFF.

ISN'T SHE PRETTY?

HA HA!

ARE YOU PICKING EINSTEIN'S NOSE?

NO!!

HEH--

WHAT A DUNCE.

MAL?

I SUPPOSE THE MAIN PURPOSE OF GOING TO SCHOOL IS TO GAIN SPECIALIZED KNOWLEDGE IN ORDER TO ENABLE ONE TO SECURE MORE PROFITABLE OR DESIRED OCCUPATIONS.

SCIENCE FAIR!

JOIN!

UH...

I MEAN--

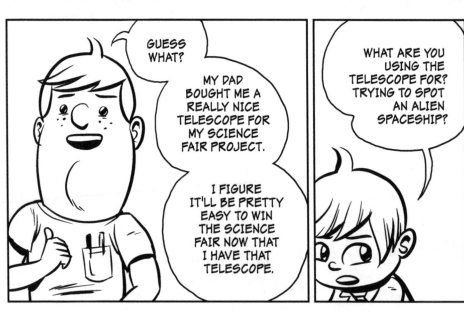

POOR CAPTAIN PORKY...

CAPTAIN PORKY?

≥sniff≤

I CAN'T EAT RIGHT NOW. YOU WANT THIS COOKIE?

24

CHAPTER 2
Don't Be Such A Cry-Puppy!

WHY DO YOU GO TO SCHOOL, ANYWAY?

STRANGE. MY TEACHER ASKED ME THAT SAME QUESTION TODAY.

I MEAN, YOU ALREADY KNOW EVERYTHING THERE IS TO KNOW ABOUT EVERYTHING! WHAT MORE CAN YOU LEARN AT ELEMENTARY SCHOOL?

CHAD, WE CAN'T LET ANYONE KNOW HOW SMART I AM. IF PEOPLE KNEW I WAS SMART ENOUGH TO GO TO COLLEGE, THEY'D MAKE ME *GO* TO COLLEGE.

THEN I'D HAVE TO DO ALL SORTS OF BORING ADULT STUFF. AND I DON'T WANT TO GROW UP--

I'D RATHER BE A KID!

I KNOW WHAT THE REAL REASON IS-- IF THEY TOOK YOU OUT OF ELEMENTARY SCHOOL, YOU WOULDN'T GET TO SEE THAT GIRL YOU LIKE!

!

YOU-- I-- WHAT GIRL? MEGAN? I DON'T LIKE MEGAN!

YOU DO! YOU DO TOO!

AAARGH!

AREN'T WE DONE YET? WE'VE BEEN WORKING ON THIS FOR MONTHS.

WE'VE GOT EVERYTHING DONE EXCEPT FOR THE CONE.

THE PROBLEM IS, I HAVE NO IDEA WHERE WE'RE GOING TO GET A ROCKET CONE.

WELL, THAT'S OKAY. WE'LL THINK OF SOMETHING LATER. LET'S DO SOMETHING FUN TODAY! I'M TIRED OF WORKING ON THE ROCKET.

I HAVE TO DO HOMEWORK...

WHAT? I THOUGHT YOU ALWAYS FINISHED YOUR HOMEWORK ON THE BUS!

WELL, THIS HOMEWORK IS HARD. I'M SUPPOSED TO DECIDE WHAT I WANT TO BE WHEN I GROW UP.

BUT HOW AM I SUPPOSED TO KNOW?

OOH! WHAT IF WE USED THE TIME MACHINE TO GO INTO THE FUTURE AND SEE WHAT YOU BECOME WHEN YOU GROW UP?

NO. WE DON'T WANT TO CREATE ANY TIME PARADOXES, AND SEEING YOUR FUTURE SELF IS DEFINITELY ONE WAY TO DO THAT.

HMMM...

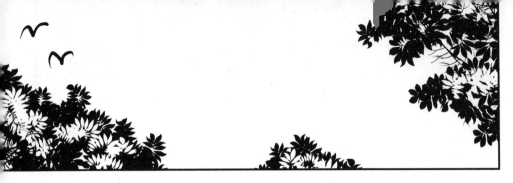

HOW ABOUT A SCUBA DIVER?

WHAT?

WHAT IF YOU BECAME A PROFESSIONAL SCUBA DIVER WHEN YOU GROW UP? YOU KNOW, UNDERWATER EXPLORATION AND STUFF?

HMMM...

I'VE NEVER THOUGHT ABOUT THAT BEFORE.

...BUT I SUPPOSE WE COULD GIVE IT A TRY-- IN FACT, WE COULD TRY IT OUT RIGHT NOW!

AND IF I LIKE IT, THAT'S WHAT I'LL WRITE MY SHORT ESSAY ABOUT!

YEAH!

WAIT. HOW ARE WE GOING TO GO SCUBA DIVING IF THERE'S NO WATER FOR MILES AROUND?

I THINK I'VE GOT JUST THE INVENTION! MEET ME IN THE KITCHEN!

THE KITCHEN?

YEP.

OKAY...

NOW, WHERE DID I PUT THOSE LOLLIPOPS?

RIGHT HERE.

OKAY. NOW I'M **REALLY** CONFUSED.

IF WE WANT TO DISCOVER WHAT DEEP-SEA EXPLORATION IS LIKE, WE NEED A DEEP SEA, RIGHT?

YEAH, BUT THIS IS JUST A SINK FULL OF DIRTY DISHWATER.

THIS WATER IS PROBABLY CLEANER THAN OCEAN WATER.

NO, MY POINT IS THAT THIS SINK FULL OF WATER WOULD ONLY BE A DEEP SEA TO SOMEONE WHO IS ABOUT HALF AN INCH TALL...

EXACTLY! NOW, OBSERVE...

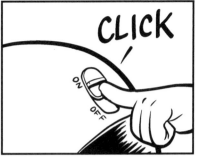

CLICK

ON
OFF

VREEEEEE

WHAT ARE YOU DOING WITH MOM'S OLD VACUUM CLEANER?

VREEEEEE

I MODIFIED IT. NOW IT'S A MINI-MEGA-MORPHER!

A WHAT?

JUST WATCH!

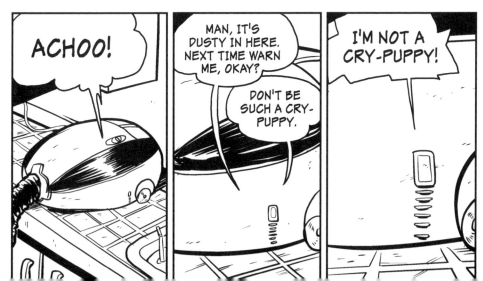

CREAK!

HEY--

CHECK IT OUT!

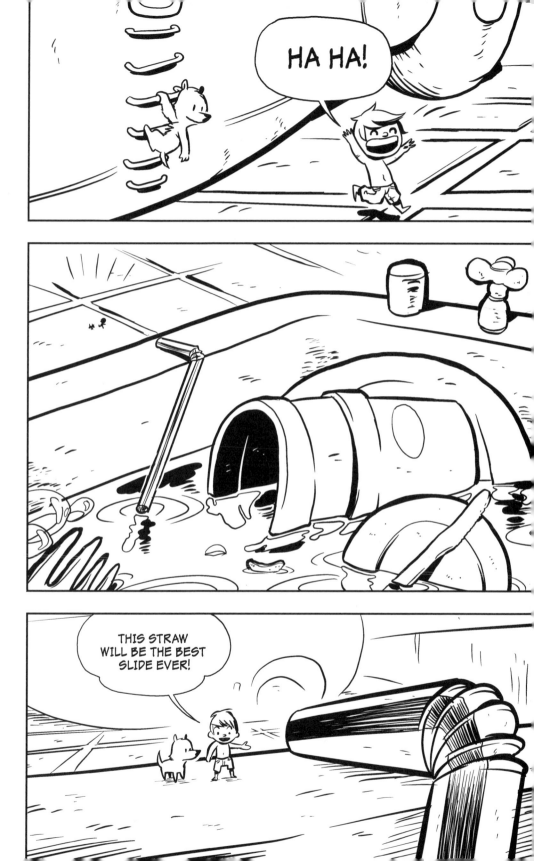

SORRY, BUT I'M TIRED OF GETTING SUCKED THROUGH TUBES.

COME ON! IT'LL BE LIKE A WATERSLIDE!

WHAT IF WE, UM...

I THOUGHT YOU SAID YOU WEREN'T A CRY-PUPPY!

I'M *NOT A* CRY-PUPPY!

WELL, COME ON!

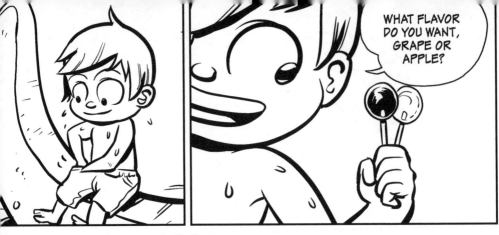

WHAT? DIDN'T YOUR MOM SAY WE'RE NOT ALLOWED TO SLAM DOORS?

I THINK IT *IS* MOM. SHE'S HOME EARLY.

MAL? ARE YOU HOME?

ACK!

WE'VE GOT TO GET BACK TO THE MINI-MEGA-MORPHER!

HE MUST BE PLAYING OUT IN HIS TREE FORT.

BOOM BOOM BOOM

WHAT WAS HE DOING WITH MY OLD VACUUM CLEANER?

AND HE'S FORGOTTEN TO DO THE DISHES!

NO MATTER HOW MANY TIMES I ASK THAT BOY...

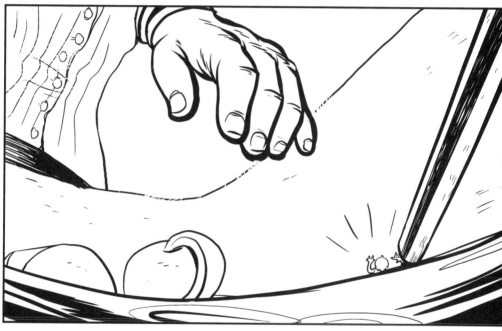

KOFF KOFF

PWAF

I GUESS I FORGOT TO TAKE THE DIRT BAG OUT!

MAL? IS THAT YOU?

AH--

UH... WELCOME HOME, MOM!

DID YOU RIG THAT VACUUM CLEANER AS SOME KIND OF PRANK, MAL?

UM... APRIL FOOLS? HEH HEH--

I'M SORRY, MOM.

VERY FUNNY. FIRST, HELP ME CLEAN THE KITCHEN. SECOND, TAKE A BATH. AND THEN INTO BED WITHOUT DINNER.

HEY! WHAT IF WE SHRANK DOWN AND SWAM HERE IN THE BATHTUB? THAT'D PROBABLY BE CLEANER THAN THE SINK.

IT'S OKAY. I'M PRETTY SURE I DON'T WANT TO BE A DEEP-SEA EXPLORER ANYMORE.

AT LEAST YOUR MOM HASN'T FOUND OUT ABOUT THE HOLE WE MADE IN THE CEILING THIS MORNING.

MAL! WHY DID YOU PUT A POSTER ON YOUR CEILING?

CHAPTER 3
Tastes Like a Meat Cheerio!

THERE'S SOMETHING STRANGE IN THE UPPER ATMOSPHERE...

THERE'S SOMETHING FLYING AROUND UP THERE!

GOT TO INCREASE MAGNIFICATION...

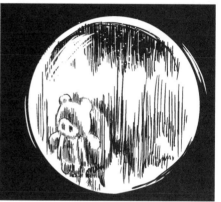

IS THAT A--

ALIEN!

...AND WE WERE OUT OF PEANUT BUTTER.

SWEETIE, YOU'RE NOT SUPPOSED TO FEED THE DOG HUMAN FOOD. DOGS EAT DOG FOOD.

BUT HE DOESN'T LIKE DOG FOOD! HE THINKS IT'S YUCKY!

MAL, YOU NEED TO LEARN TO TAKE CARE OF YOUR DOG PROPERLY.

AND THEN SHE SAID SHE'D GROUND ME IF SHE FINDS OUT I'VE BEEN FEEDING YOU HUMAN FOOD AGAIN.

BUT DOG FOOD IS YUCKY!

CHAD

IT CAN'T BE THAT BAD. IT SAYS HERE THIS FOOD'S MADE FOR A DOG'S PALATE.

HAPPY DOG FOOD

YOU TRY SOME! IT'S GROSS!

HAPPY DOG FOOD

IF I EAT A PIECE, WILL YOU EAT THE REST?

IF YOU EAT A PIECE AND TELL ME YOU LIKE IT, THEN I'LL EAT THE REST. BUT IF YOU DON'T LIKE IT, THEN YOU HAVE TO EAT THE REST.

MUNCH

MUNCH

KRUNCH

chew

chew

chew

GASP!

KOFF KOFF

IT TASTES LIKE A MEAT CHEERIO!

GULP

AHEM, I MEAN...

I LIKE IT!

YOU DO? WELL, GREAT! WHY DON'T YOU HAVE ANOTHER PIECE?

CHAPTER 4
Megan's Flaming Dodge Bomb

ZACHARY!

YOU TAKE A TIME-OUT!

WHAT?

WHY?

YOU'VE BEEN UP TO BAT MORE THAN ANYBODY ELSE. WHY DON'T WE LET SOMEONE ELSE TRY?

BUT THIS IS A CRUCIAL KICK! IF WE DON'T GET OUR RUNNERS HOME, THE GIRLS WILL BEAT US!

WELL, PERHAPS YOU BOYS SHOULDN'T HAVE CHALLENGED THE GIRLS IN THE FIRST PLACE.

MALCOM, WHY DON'T YOU TRY? YOU'VE ONLY BEEN UP ONCE.

BUT I--

THE DUNCE CAN'T KICK, COACH!

SIT DOWN, ZACHARY.

WAVE

VWOOSH!

HEY, DUNCE! I'VE GOT A QUESTION FOR YOU.

WHAT?

ARE YOU PLANNING ON ENTERING THE SCIENCE FAIR?

ARE YOU AFRAID THAT IF I ENTERED, I'D WIN?

ARE YOU KIDDING?

YOU WOULDN'T STAND A CHANCE AGAINST MY INTELLECT!

IT'S JUST THAT, UM, DUE TO CERTAIN CIRCUMSTANCES, I RECENTLY DECIDED TO DO MY SCIENCE FAIR PROJECT ON ALIENS.

BUT BEFORE I STARTED, I WANTED TO MAKE SURE THAT YOU WEREN'T ALREADY DOING A PROJECT ABOUT ALIENS.

IT'D BE A DISASTER IF WE DID THE SAME PROJECT...

OH... WELL...
I WASN'T PLANNING ON EVEN ENTERING THE SCIENCE FAIR...

UNLESS...

DON'T LET ANYONE EAT MY LUNCH! I'LL BE RIGHT BACK!

heh heh.

SUCKER.

CHOMP!

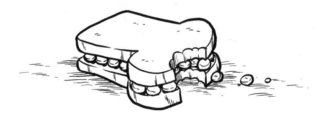

CHAPTER 5
Ugly Rubber Duckling

DO YOU FEEL LIKE TRYING TO FIGURE OUT WHAT YOU WANT TO BE WHEN YOU GROW UP?

OH YEAH...

I FORGOT...

THAT ASSIGNMENT IS DUE TOMORROW.

I THINK I FOUND THE PERFECT JOB FOR YOU...

WHAT IS IT?

slap!

HOW ABOUT AN ARCHAEOLOGIST?

CERATOSAURUS DISCOVERY

ON DISPLAY AT MUSEUM

THE WOMAN WHO DISCOVERED THIS DINOSAUR IS REALLY FAMOUS NOW.

WHAT MAKES IT AMAZING IS THAT SHE DISCOVERED A COMPLETE SKELETON...

WELL, ALL EXCEPT THAT HORN, I GUESS.

HMMM... EXCAVATING DINOSAUR BONES IS A LOT OF WORK, AND I DON'T WANT TO GET DIRTY LIKE WE DID YESTERDAY.

WAIT!

I'VE GOT AN IDEA!

WHAT?

MAYBE IT'S FINALLY TIME TO USE THE *TIME MACHINE!*

WHY DIG UP DINOSAURS WHEN YOU CAN SEE THEM IN THE FLESH?

LET'S DO IT!

THIS ELEVATOR HAS COME A LONG WAY SINCE WE FOUND IT IN THE JUNKYARD.

I PACKED THE FOOD. ARE YOU READY?

YEP! LET'S GO!

1 10 100

TIME JUMP

CLICK

CLOSE

bing!

WHAT'S THAT?

OUR UGLY RUBBER DUCKLING BATH TOY?

WITH A SLIGHT MODIFICATION, OF COURSE.

SQEEZE!

PFLUMP!

AUTO-INFLATING DUCKY BOAT.

SWEET!

SPLASH!

THERE ARE SOME AMAZING CREATURES DOWN THERE!

WE'RE GETTING CLOSE. CAN YOU LOOK DOWN THERE AND SEE WHAT THOSE THINGS ARE?

OH YEAH! I'LL CHECK.

sploosh!

LET'S GET OFF AT THAT PALM TREE!

SQUEEZE—

POP

HOLD ON TIGHT!

UH, WAIT A SEC. ARE YOU GOING TO--

--JUMP?

PSSH!

YOU BROUGHT DOG FOOD TOO?

YEP. AND I ALSO WHIPPED UP THIS!

YUM SAUCE

IT'S CALLED YUM SAUCE.

I INVENTED IT YESTERDAY. IT MAKES ANYTHING TASTE LIKE YOUR FAVORITE FOOD. YOU CAN USE IT FROM NOW ON FOR MEALS.

sniff

YOU'RE THE BEST, MAL!

WE SHOULD PROBABLY GO HOME SOON. WON'T YOUR MOM WONDER WHERE WE ARE?

WE'LL GET BACK THE INSTANT WE LEFT, SO WE'LL BE FINE. BUT I SUPPOSE WE'D BETTER MAKE OUR WAY BACK TO THE TIME MACHINE.

NOW THAT THE SUN'S GONE DOWN, THE JUNGLE'S GOTTEN SORT OF CREEPY...

DON'T WORRY, I BROUGHT JUST THE THING.

IS THAT THE SWISS ARMY KNIFE YOUR MOM GOT YOU FOR CHRISTMAS?

YEAH, EXCEPT I MODIFIED IT A LITTLE BIT. NOW IT'S GOT A LOT MORE INSIDE OF IT THAN THE USUAL SWISS ARMY KNIFE.

SNKK!

I CALL IT THE ÜBER-KNIFE!

NOW WE'LL BE ABLE TO FIND OUR WAY BACK TO THE TIME MACHINE EASILY ENOUGH.

CLICK

COOL!

ARE YOU SURE THIS IS THE WAY?

YEAH. I'M PRETTY SURE WE CAME OUT THIS WAY.

I DON'T REMEMBER THAT ROCK BEING THERE.

PANG!

ERRGH!

PFOING!

AARRGH!

I KNOW I'VE GOT SOMETHING THAT WILL HELP US--

WAIT! HERE'S SOMETHING WE CAN USE!

HOLD ON TIGHT, CHAD!

CREAK

PHEW!

MAL, I WANT TO GO HOME. I'M REALLY SCARED NOW.

CLICK

IT'LL BE OKAY, CHAD.

VREEE

KNCH

WE'VE JUST GOT TO GET BACK TO THE TIME MACHINE AND--

WHAT IS IT?

CHAPTER 6
But Mal, Think of the Omelets!

124

BUT WHAT IF WE GET EATEN?

WELL, I DON'T KNOW ABOUT YOU, BUT I STILL SMELL A BIT LIKE THE INSIDE OF A VACUUM CLEANER.

NO DINOSAUR WOULD WANT TO EAT SOMETHING AS DIRTY AS WE ARE--

WHAT WAS THAT?!

WHAT?

DIDN'T YOU HEAR THAT JUST NOW?

C'MON, CHAD, DON'T SCARE ME LIKE THA--

HOW ARE WE GOING TO SLEEP HERE?

DO YOU HAVE AN ENTIRE TENT IN YOUR BRIEFCASE?

NO, BUT I DO HAVE THIS!

A SEED?

MAL, I HATE TO BREAK IT TO YOU, BUT THIS IS NOT A GOOD TIME TO PLANT A GARDEN.

JUST WATCH...

fppt

IT LOOKS JUST LIKE ONE OF THE DAISIES THAT GROW BY THE STREAM NEAR OUR HOUSE...

YEP. BUT I GENETICALLY MODIFIED THIS PARTICULAR DAISY. JUST KEEP WATCHING...

I CALL IT A DAISY WIGWAM.

QUICK, GET INSIDE! I THINK I JUST FELT A RAINDROP!

I'M OVER HERE!

huff huff

huff huff

DON'T LEAVE LIKE THAT! THAT WAS REALLY SCARY.

I'M SORRY! I COULDN'T SLEEP AND SO I DECIDED TO GO EXPLORE A LITTLE BIT.

AND LOOK! I FOUND BREAKFAST!

ISN'T THIS GREAT? WE CAN MAKE THE BIGGEST OMELET EVER! AND YOUR MOM WON'T GET MAD!

UM... WHERE'D YOU FIND THIS?

I FOUND A WHOLE LOT MORE IN A BIG PILE A LITTLE WAYS OVER THERE! I'VE BEEN TRYING TO ROLL THIS ONE BACK TO OUR CAMPSITE, BUT IT'S HEAVY.

CHAD! THAT WAS A NEST! YOU CAN'T TAKE A DINOSAUR EGG OUT OF A NEST!

WHY NOT?

IT'S DANGEROUS! IF THE MOTHER OF THIS EGG SEES US, SHE'LL KILL US!

RUN! WE'VE GOT TO FIND THE TIME MACHINE!

BUT MAL! WE CAN'T ABANDON THIS DINOSAUR HERE! IT'S JUST A BABY!

CRACK!

SQUEAK!

THAT'S NOT JUST A BABY DINOSAUR, THAT'S A BABY ANKYLOSAURUS!

IF THE MOTHER DINOSAUR FINDS US HERE, WE'LL BE EATEN ALIVE.

NO! NO NAMING IT! NO DINOSAUR PETS!

WE'VE GOT TO GO!

DON'T TELL ME YOU'RE GOING TO LEAVE POOR CHARLIE ALL ALONE HERE!

RaAAA

WELL, IT'S EITHER THAT OR DYING IN THE JAWS OF AN ANGRY MOTHER ANKYLOSAURUS!

FINE! WE'LL TAKE HIM BACK TO HIS NEST, BUT THEN WE HAVE TO GO HOME!

STUPID PUPPY-DOG EYES...

PEEKABOO!

HEY! CHARLIE LOVES TO PLAY PEEKABOO!

RARF RARF RARF

STOP PLAYING WITH HIM!

OKAY, SO WHERE'S THIS NEST?

IT WAS AROUND HERE SOMEWHERE... IT SHOULD BE EASY TO SPOT WITH ALL THOSE EGGS INSIDE.

OH NO.

MAL! CHECK IT OUT!

YOU OKAY, CHAD?

YEAH... HEY, WEREN'T WE SUPPOSED TO REAPPEAR AT THE SAME SPOT WE LEFT?

I GUESS THE TIME MACHINE HAD TROUBLE NAVIGATING AFTER IT WAS DAMAGED BY THAT ANKYLOSAURUS. BUT THAT'S NOT OUR BIGGEST PROBLEM--

WHAT?

IT LOOKS LIKE THE TIME MACHINE HAS BROUGHT US BACK ABOUT TWO HOURS AFTER WE LEFT!

WE'RE LATE FOR DINNER!

YOUR MOM'S GOING TO KILL US! WHAT SHOULD WE DO WITH ALL THIS WRECKAGE?

WE'LL CLEAN IT UP TOMORROW AFTER SCHOOL.

COME ON!

CHAPTER 7
The Super-duper-intendent

CHAD, WOULD YOU COME TO SCHOOL WITH ME? I MEAN, FOR SHOW-AND-TELL?

WHY?

I DON'T KNOW... I WAS THINKING IT'D BE COOL TO SHOW YOU TO THE CLASS... MAYBE DO SOME TRICKS...

I'LL PASS.

PLEASE! PLEASE! PLEASE! PLEASE! **PLEEEEASE!**

WHY DO YOU WANT ME TO GO SO BAD?

OH, NO REASON, I JUST--

AH... YOU WANT TO IMPRESS MEGAN, DON'T YOU?

NO! THAT'S--

THAT-- UM,

I DON'T--

I'LL GO ON ONE CONDITION.

ADMIT TO ME THAT YOU LIKE HER.

I'LL-- I-- I--

HA HA. I'LL GO. I JUST WANTED TO SEE THE TERROR IN YOUR FACE.

CHAD!

HA HA!

AND NEXT UP IS MALCOM. COME ON UP, MALCOM.

YOUR DOG IS SO CUTE, MAL.

AHEM.

THIS IS MY DOG, CHAD. I GOT CHAD WHEN I WAS REALLY YOUNG.

BACK THEN, MY FAMILY MOVED AROUND A LOT, SO CHAD WAS MY ONLY FRIEND.

SINCE WE SPENT A LOT OF TIME TOGETHER, I TAUGHT HIM ALL SORTS OF TRICKS.

WHAT KIND OF TRICKS DID YOU TEACH HIM?

WELL, HEH HEH... I TAUGHT CHAD HOW TO SIT AND CATCH FRISBEES AND FETCH STICKS...

THAT'S LAME. EVERY DOG KNOWS HOW TO DO THAT.

BUT, UH, I ALSO TAUGHT HIM HOW TO PLAY CARDS, AND USE THE TELEPHONE, AND EAT WITH CHOPSTICKS!

REALLY?

THAT'S IMPOSSIBLE! DOGS CAN'T USE THE TELEPHONE. DOGS CAN'T TALK!

THAT'S NOT TRUE! I TAUGHT CHAD HOW TO TALK USING A SPECIAL INVENTION I MADE!

WAIT. WHY DOES CHAD HAVE TO GO TO THE TEACHERS' LOUNGE?

A DOG IS TOO DISTRACTING TO HAVE IN THE CLASSROOM.

BUT YOUR DOG SEEMS EXCEPTIONALLY WELL BEHAVED, SO I THINK HE'LL BE FINE THERE.

YOU CAN GET HIM BACK AFTER SCHOOL ENDS.

IT'S OKAY, CHAD. YOU GO WITH MEGAN. I'LL SEE YOU LATER.

IT'S JUST THAT

"WHAT DO I WANT TO BE WHEN I GROW UP?"

SEEMS LIKE A TRICK QUESTION...

IT FEELS LIKE THERE'S SOMETHING I'VE BEEN MISSING...

HMMM.

WELL, I'LL GIVE YOU ANOTHER DAY SINCE YOU'RE USUALLY SO GOOD ABOUT TURNING THINGS IN. BUT DON'T DISAPPOINT ME AGAIN, ALL RIGHT?

OKAY.

167

ZACHARY! YOU SCARED ME! WHY DIDN'T YOU COME TO CLASS THIS MORNING?

I'VE BEEN WORKING ON OUR SCIENCE FAIR PROJECT.

YOU DIDN'T DO ALL THE WORK WITHOUT ME, DID YOU?

I FOUND AN ALIEN SPACE-SHIP.

WHAT?

I SAW IT CRASH-LAND, BUT WHEN I CAME TO THE SITE, THE SPACECRAFT WAS ALL IN PIECES.

SO I SPENT ALL NIGHT PUTTING IT BACK TOGETHER!

YOU'RE KIDDING-- LET ME SEE!

IT'S IN THE GYM. I PULLED IT TO SCHOOL ON MY WAGON SO THAT WE COULD SET IT UP IN A DISPLAY FOR THE FAIR.

I STILL CAN'T BELIEVE THIS. WHERE DID YOU FIND A CRASH-LANDED UFO?

IN SOME ABANDONED LOT. IT LOOKED LIKE IT--

CLACK

UH-OH.

SIGH.

THIS COULD BE THE WORST DAY OF MY LIFE. WHY ARE PEOPLE SO MEAN?

I SUPPOSE EVEN YOU COULDN'T ANSWER THAT QUESTION, EINSTEIN.

WAIT A MINUTE!

MEGAN WASN'T BEING MEAN LIKE THE REST OF THE KIDS!

SHE LOOKED...

SAD.

WHAT WAS SHE SAD ABOUT?

HELLO?

THIS IS THE SUPERINTENDENT. I NEED YOU TO COME TO THE TEACHERS' LOUNGE IMMEDIATELY.

THIS DOESN'T SOUND LIKE THE SUPERINTENDENT.

THAT'S BECAUSE I'M THE **SUPER-DUPER-INTENDENT!** NOW COME TO THE TEACHERS' LOUNGE AT ONCE! IT APPEARS THAT THE DOG YOU SENT HERE HAS BEEN EATING THE DOUGHNUTS!

THAT IS ALL!

SLAM!

?

174

175

THERE'S ELEVATOR MUSIC COMING OUT OF THIS BROKEN SPEAKER...

HA HA! THIS IS TOTALLY AN ELEVATOR!

I'M TELLING YOU, THOUGH, I **SAW** IT EXPLODE AND FALL OUT OF THE SKY!

YOU TOLD ME ON THE WAY OVER YOU WERE SLEEPING WHEN THE EXPLOSION WOKE YOU UP-- BUT WHAT IF YOU DREAMED THE WHOLE CRASH-LANDING THING?

DREAMED IT?

SURE. THIS ELEVATOR WAS PROBABLY JUST GARBAGE SOMEONE LEFT IN THAT OLD ABANDONED LOT, AND YOU JUST HAPPENED TO FIND IT BY CHANCE.

AH!

MEGAN... LOOKED SAD...

BECAUSE SHE FELT BAD FOR ME...

MAYBE SHE EVEN...

TEE HEE.

THIS COULD BE THE BEST DAY OF MY LIFE!

MAL!

YOU'VE GOTTA COME QUICK!

WHAT IS IT?

I THINK ZACHARY'S GOT OUR TIME MACHINE!

CHAPTER 8
Peekabooasaurus

YOU DIDN'T CALL ME DUNCE! ARE YOU OKAY?

YEAH. I FEEL WONDERFUL!

YOU DON'T LOOK WONDERFUL.

JUST LOOK AROUND YOU, MAL... WE'RE IN THE DINOSAUR AGE! DO YOU KNOW WHAT THAT MEANS?

UM...

WE MIGHT GET EATEN BY DINOSAURS IF WE DON'T GET OUT OF HERE?

IT MEANS THAT ALTHOUGH THIS ISN'T AN ALIEN SPACESHIP, IT'S NO ORDINARY ELEVATOR EITHER! THIS IS A TIME MACHINE! AND DO YOU KNOW WHAT THAT MEANS?

UM...

WE MIGHT GET EATEN BY DINOSAURS IF WE DON'T GET OUT OF HERE?

IT MEANS THAT I'M SO SMART, I BUILT A TIME MACHINE OUT OF OLD ELEVATOR PARTS WITHOUT EVEN KNOWING IT! I MUST BE A GENIUS! AND DO YOU KNOW WHAT THAT MEANS?

WE'RE DEFINITELY GOING TO BE EATEN BY DINOSAURS.

WITH A PROJECT LIKE THIS, I'LL NOT ONLY WIN THE SCHOOL SCIENCE FAIR, I'LL WIN THE STATE AND NATIONAL SCIENCE FAIRS TOO!

I'LL BE FAMOUS!

ZACHARY, YOU OBVIOUSLY DIDN'T MAKE A TIME MACHINE THAT WORKED! YOU'VE RIPPED A HOLE IN TIME!

I'M A GENIUS! I'LL FIGURE... SOMETHING... OUT...

IS HE DEAD?

NO. HE JUST PASSED OUT. COME ON, LET'S GET HIM OUT OF HERE.

HEY, LOOK! THE HOLE IN TIME IS GETTING SMALLER!

OH NO, WE'D BETTER HURRY!

WAIT...

WHAT IS IT?

MEGAN WAS WITH ME...

I THINK SHE GOT CHASED OFF BY A DINOSAUR.

WHAT?!

fzzt!

OKAY, I THINK WE LOST IT...

MAL, THERE'S A DINOSAUR RIGHT BEHIND YOU!

YEEK!

RARF
RARF
RARF

IT'S CHARLIE!

YOU WERE PLAYING PEEKABOO WITH ME, WEREN'T YOU?

RERF.

WHAT ARE YOU TALKING ABOUT?! ARE YOU INSANE?

UM, UH...

I SAID THIS IS A... A *PEEKABOOASAURUS!* IT'S... UM... FRIENDLY!

YOU'RE A NICE DINOSAUR, AREN'T YOU?

SQUACK!

SHHHH!

RUSTLE

KSSH!

I DON'T WANT TO DIE.

ERF

BANG!

WOW, ZACHARY ACTUALLY DIDN'T DO TOO BAD OF A JOB REPAIRING THIS...

TIME JUMP

ROAR!

MAL! IT'S CHARGING!

QUICK! JUMP IN!

TIME JUMP

WE'RE BACK.

WOW. I CAN'T BELIEVE ZACHARY ACTUALLY BUILT A TIME MACHINE! HE REALLY IS A GENIUS, ISN'T HE?

YEAH... I GUESS.

WE'D BETTER GET HIM TO THE SCHOOL NURSE TO SEE IF HE'S OKAY...

ARE YOU ALL RIGHT, MAL?

DOESN'T LOOK LIKE ZACHARY WILL BE ABLE TO REBUILD THE TIME MACHINE OUT OF THIS WRECKAGE.

HEY! WHAT'S THIS?

OH, THAT'S A DINOSAUR HORN. IT'S A LONG STORY.

WHAT ARE YOU GOING TO DO WITH IT? WE COULD TAKE IT TO THE MUSEUM AND BECOME FAMOUS!

CHAPTER 9
The Biggest, Bestest Day

the
end